Collins

AQA GCSE 9

Food Preparation and Nutrition

Food Preparation and Nutrition

AQA GCSE 9-1

Workbook

Kath Callaghan, Fiona Balding, Barbara Monks,
Barbara Rathmill and Suzanne Gray with Louise T. Davies

Contents

Food Preparation Skills

Knife Skills   4
Fish   5
Meat   6
Prepare, Combine and Shape   7
Dough   8

Food Nutrition and Health

Protein and Fat   9
Carbohydrate   10
Vitamins   11
Minerals and Water   12
Making Informed Choices   13
Diet, Nutrition and Health   14

Food Science

Cooking of Food, Heat Transfer and Selecting Appropriate Cooking Methods   15
Proteins and Enzymic Browning   16
Carbohydrates   17
Fats and Oils   18
Raising Agents   19

Food Safety

Microorganisms, Enzymes and Food Spoilage   20
Microorganisms in Food Production   21
Bacterial Contamination   22
Buying and Storing Food   23
Preparing and Cooking Food   24

Factors Affecting Food Choice

Food Choices   25
British and International Cuisines   26
Sensory Evaluation   27
Food Labelling   28
Factors Affecting Food Choice   29

Contents

Food Provenance

Food and the Environment   30
Food Provenance and Production Methods   31
Sustainability of Food   32
Food Production   33
Food Processing   34

Practice Exam Paper 1   35
Practice Exam Paper 2   52

Answers   69

1 Which type of knife is shown in the picture? Tick (✓) **one** answer.

a) Paring knife ☐   b) Cook's knife ☐

c) Filleting knife ☐   d) Palette knife ☐   [1]

2 When boning a chicken, what colour board should you use? Tick (✓) **one** answer.

a) Blue ☐   b) Red ☐

c) Green ☐   d) Brown ☐   [1]

3 A chef or professional cook has their own set of knives that are really the 'tools of the trade' and they learn to use them and look after them when training.

Name and describe the **two** main methods of cutting that are the basis of a cook's knife handling skills. [4]

	Knife Hold: ....
	Explanation: ....
	Knife Hold: ....
	Explanation: ....

4 Explain **four** safety rules to observe when working with knives in the kitchen.

....

....

....

....

[4]

Total Marks .... / 10

1 Which of the following fish would you expect to find preserved in a can? Tick (✓) **one** answer.

a) Cod ☐   b) Plaice ☐   c) Sardine ☐   d) Halibut ☐   [1]

2 Which of the following fish is a mollusc? Tick (✓) **one** answer.

a) Oyster ☐   b) Crab ☐   c) Shrimp ☐   d) Lobster ☐   [1]

3 Which choice would NOT be suitable when enrobing a fish fillet before cooking?
Tick (✓) **one** answer.

a) Breadcrumbs ☐   b) Polenta ☐

c) Batter ☐   d) Chocolate ☐   [1]

4 In what **two** ways can fish be protected when cooked in hot fat?

_____ [2]

5 Complete the following statements using the words in the boxes below.

| collagen | 60 °C | coagulate | muscle | gelatine | connective tissue |

Fish cooks quickly because the _____ is short and the

_____ is thin.

The connective tissue is made up of _____ and will change into

_____ and _____ at

_____ .   [6]

6 The picture below shows a fish being filleted. Complete the table below.

| | Classification of the fish shown:

_____ [1]

One example of this type of fish:

_____ [1] | What is the chef showing?

_____
_____
_____
_____
_____ [2] |

Meat

1 Which of these nutrients is **not** found in meat? Tick (✓) **one** answer.

a) Fat ☐ **b)** Vitamin B6 ☐ **c)** Protein ☐ **d)** Vitamin C ☐ [1]

2 Which meat is classed as offal? Tick (✓) **one** answer.

a) Pork ☐ **b)** Poultry ☐ **c)** Liver ☐ **d)** Goose ☐ [1]

3 What is meat? Complete the following sentence using the words in the boxes below.

| muscle | connective tissue | fibres |

Meat is a .... composed of cells consisting of

.... , held together by .... [3]

4 Name **one** part of an animal that is likely to be tougher to eat.

.... [1]

5 Name **two** slow methods of cooking that are suitable for tough cuts of meat.

.... [2]

6 Complete the following sentences about what happens when meat is cooked. Use the words in the boxes below.

| Maillard | gelatine | coagulate | browning | sugars |

The .... of meat is caused by a reaction with natural .... and

proteins to produce a dark colour. This occurrence is called the .... reaction or

non-enzymic browning.

As the meat cooks the proteins .... and produce a firm texture. Collagen is

broken down into .... [5]

Total Marks .... / 13

1 Which glaze would be most suitable for a batch of Chelsea buns? Tick (✓) **one** answer.

   a) Egg wash ☐   **b)** Arrowroot ☐

   c) Sugar and water ☐   **d)** Egg yolk ☐   [1]

2 What type of binding agent is generally used in a sausage mixture? Tick (✓) **one** answer.

   a) Breadcrumbs ☐   **b)** Flour ☐

   c) Egg ☐   **d)** Water ☐   [1]

3 In baking, what is the difference between stirring and whisking?

   ....

   ....   [2]

4 In baking, what is the advantage of using cutters and a rolling pin when making a batch of biscuits?

   ....

   ....   [2]

5 Explain which mixing and shaping skills can be used when making a decorated Victoria sandwich cake to give a quality finish.

   ....

   ....

   ....

   ....

   ....

   ....   [8]

6 How would you make sure that a batch of burgers are all exactly the same size and shape?

   ....

   ....   [2]

Total Marks .... / 16

1 What is gluten? Tick (✓) **one** answer.

a) A leavening agent ☐

b) A sweetener ☐

c) A protein found in flour ☐

d) A muscle ☐ [1]

2 What is enriched dough? Tick (✓) **one** answer.

a) A dough that contains organic ingredients. ☐

b) A dough that has additional sugar and butter added. ☐

c) A dough that has extra ingredients added, such as herbs or cheese. ☐

d) A dough that contains expensive ingredients. ☐ [1]

3 What is the name of the method used to make shortcrust pastry?

.... [1]

4 What is the function of water in a shortcrust pastry?

.... [1]

5 Use the words in the boxes to complete the stages in the choux pastry method.

| cool | accurately | rolling boil | heavy dropping |

| fat | flour | water | paste |

Weigh all the ingredients ....

Place .... and .... in a pan and bring

to a ....

Add sieved .... immediately and mix well to form a

....

.... then add beaten eggs gradually to a

.... consistency. Cook in a hot oven. [8]

6 What are the names of the **two** proteins found in strong plain flour used in making bread?

.... [2]

Total Marks .... / 14

Protein and Fat

1 Fill in the missing words.

The body needs protein for g............................., maintenance and r......................... [2]

2 Give **two** different protein foods suitable for a lacto-vegetarian.

.... [2]

3 Give **three** examples of protein foods that have a High Biological Value (HBV).

.... [3]

4 Underline the food that is a good example of protein complementation.

Jam sandwich   **Lentil soup and bread**   **Tomato and basil salad**   **Sausage roll**   [1]

5 What is the name of the protein deficiency disease? Tick (✓) **one** answer.

a) Beri-beri ☐   **b)** Scurvy ☐   **c)** Kwashiorkor ☐   **d)** Dermatitis ☐   [1]

6 Give **one** example of a fat in liquid form.

.... [1]

7 Which of the following are functions of fat in the diet? Underline **two** answers.

Provides concentrated energy   **Strengthens teeth**

Makes red blood cells   **Provides body with vitamins A, D, E and K**

Promotes growth   [2]

8 Which **two** components is fat made up of?

.... [2]

9 What is hydrogenation?

....

.... [1]

Total Marks .... / 15

Carbohydrate

1 What are the **three** carbohydrate groups?

....

.... [3]

2 Give an example of a monosaccharide.

.... [1]

3 Fill in the missing words.

Sugars are d .... very quickly in the body, providing instant e .... [2]

4 Most people in the UK do not eat enough dietary fibre. Suggest a similar food that is higher in dietary fibre to replace each of those listed below.

a) White bread ....

b) Cornflakes ....

c) Mashed potato .... [3]

5 Sugar, sweets and sugary drinks are associated with which type of decay in the body?

.... [1]

6 What would be the results of not eating enough carbohydrate?

....

.... [2]

7 Fill in the missing words.

St............................... have to be digested into s............................... before

a............................... – this is s............................... e............................... release. [5]

8 What is the name of the common medical condition frequently caused by a lack of dietary fibre (NSP) in the diet?

.... [1]

Total Marks .... / 18

Vitamins

1 Name **two** dietary sources of vitamin A.

_____ [2]

2 The B group vitamins and vitamin C (ascorbic acid) belong to which vitamin group?

_____ [1]

3 What is rickets and what vitamin deficiency is it associated with?

_____

_____ [2]

4 A deficiency of vitamin B2 Riboflavin can cause what deficiency symptoms? <u>Underline</u> **one** answer.

Broken and split nails   Sore throat   Vomiting   Skin cracking around the mouth   [1]

5 One of the functions of vitamin C (ascorbic acid) is to act as an antioxidant. What do antioxidants do?

_____ [1]

6 What is cholecalciferol?

_____

_____ [2]

7 Fill in the missing words.

When making a salad, to avoid the loss of vitamin C (a_____

a_____) through o_____, prepare just before

s_____ and avoid excess c_____.   [4]

8 Which vitamin deficiency can cause night blindness? Tick (✓) **one** answer.

a) Vitamin K ☐   b) Vitamin A ☐

c) Vitamin D ☐   d) Vitamin B1 ☐   [1]

Total Marks _____ / 14

Minerals and Water

1 Which vitamin helps the body to absorb calcium? Tick (✓) **one** answer.

a) Vitamin A ☐   b) Vitamin C ☐

c) Vitamin K ☐   d) Vitamin D ☐   [1]

2 Give **one** reason why calcium is needed in the body.

.... [1]

3 Name a condition that an excess of sodium (salt) in the diet is linked to.

.... [1]

4 What is salt mainly used for in food preparation?

.... [1]

5 Fill in the missing words.

A lack of iron in the diet can cause iron-deficiency a............................... and symptoms include

t............................... .   [2]

6 What is the daily recommended intake of water?

.... [1]

7 What is the function of fluoride in the diet?

....

.... [1]

8 Iodine supports the correct functioning of which gland in the body? Tick (✓) **one** answer.

a) Thyroid ☐   b) Pituitary ☐

c) Saliva ☐   d) Adrenal ☐   [1]

Total Marks .... / 9

1 Name the **five** sections of the Eatwell Guide.

_____   _____

_____   _____

_____   [5]

2 Fill in the missing words.

H_____ m_____ provides babies with all their nutritional

requirements, except for i_____. Babies are born with a supply of this stored in

their l_____.   [3]

3 What is colostrum?

_____ [1]

4 During pregnancy, why is a good supply of folate (folic acid) required?

_____

_____ [2]

5 Why are older people advised to eat lots of calcium-rich foods? Tick (✓) **one** answer.

a) To help prevent dementia ☐   **b)** To keep them hydrated ☐

c) To help strengthen bones ☐   **d)** To give them a better appetite ☐   [1]

6 Fill in the missing words.

The E_____ G_____ shows the proportions of food groups that

should be eaten daily for a w_____-b_____ diet.   [2]

7 What would you advise a pregnant woman who is suffering from constipation to do?

_____

_____ [2]

Total Marks _____ / 16

Diet, Nutrition and Health

1 Fill in the missing words.

C............................ H............................ D............................ is linked to diets high

in s............................ f............................, which make c............................ in

the blood. [3]

2 Tick (✓) **one** answer. Symptoms of iron deficiency anaemia include:

a) blurred vision and cataracts. ☐ b) sickness and diarrhoea. ☐

c) tiredness, weakness and lack of energy. ☐ d) a sore throat. ☐ [1]

3 Fruit and vegetables form part of a balanced diet. How many portions of fruit and vegetables are we advised to eat every day?

.... [1]

4 List **three** different health problems that may be linked to a high consumption of fat in the diet.

....

....

.... [3]

5 Fill in the missing words.

In Type 2 diabetes, too little or no i............................ is produced, resulting in high levels of

s............................ in the b............................. [3]

6 What is osteoporosis? Tick (✓) **one** answer.

a) Stiff neck ☐ b) When bones become weak and break easily ☐

c) Weak connective tissues ☐ d) Persistent nose bleeds ☐ [1]

7 An individual's BMR depends on **three** things. What are these three things?

.... [3]

Total Marks .... / 15

1 What does heat transfer in liquids and in air cause? Tick (✓) **one** answer.

a) Halogen currents ☐

b) Conduction currents ☐

c) Convection currents ☐

d) Induction currents ☐ [1]

2 What is cooking?

_____

_____

_____ [3]

3 Cooking methods can change the nutritional value of a food. Fill in the blanks to complete the chart.

Cooking Method	Change to Nutritional Content	Example
Dry method		Grilling sausages
Water-based (moist) method		

[3]

4 This question is about selecting appropriate cooking methods. Use the words in the boxes below to complete the sentences correctly.

| moist | hot | conserve | sensory | add | tough | quick |

Cooking methods can alter the _____ properties of food by adding crispness or softening.

The right cooking methods can _____ vitamins, or _____ energy value.

When meat needs cooking, long, slow _____ cooking is best for

_____ cuts of meat.

If the meat is tender a _____ and _____ method of cooking such as grilling can be used. [7]

Total Marks _____ / 14

Proteins and Enzymic Browning

1. Tick (✓) **one** answer. The main function of eggs in a quiche tart is:

   a) to aerate the filling. ☐   b) to add flavour. ☐

   c) to set the filling. ☐   d) to reduce the number of calories. ☐   [1]

2. Food preparation before cooking, for example marinating, is a requirement of some recipes.

   a) What is a marinade?

   ....

   ....

   .... [3]

   b) Explain why a marinade is used in cooking.

   ....

   ....

   ....

   .... [3]

   c) What might be the advantages of using a marinade for chicken kebabs?

   ....

   ....

   ....

   .... [4]

   d) Name **two** quick cooking methods that could be used to cook chicken kebabs.

   .... [2]

3. Gluten is a protein found in wheat. Which statements about gluten are **true** and which are **false**? Circle one answer for each of the parts **a)–d)**.

   a) Gluten makes dough stretchy and elastic.   **True/False**   [1]

   b) Gluten forms the structure of a baked loaf of bread.   **True/False**   [1]

   c) Salt causes gluten to be weakened.   **True/False**   [1]

   d) Gluten helps pasta hold its shape when cooked.   **True/False**   [1]

   Total Marks .... / 17

Carbohydrates

1 Which one of the following is not a sauce making method? Tick (✓) **one** answer.

a) Creaming method ☐

b) All-in-one method ☐

c) Roux method ☐

d) Blending method ☐   [1]

2 Carbohydrates are useful functional ingredients. Which of the following is not a function of carbohydrate? Tick (✓) **one** answer.

a) Caramelisation ☐

b) Coagulation ☐

c) Dextrinisation ☐

d) Gelatinisation ☐   [1]

3 A cafe needs to make macaroni cheese for lunch service. The chef uses the ingredients listed below. Give **one** main function of each of these ingredients in the macaroni cheese.

semi-skimmed milk ....

wheat flour ....

margarine ....

seasoning ....

Red Leicester cheese ....

macaroni ....   [6]

4 What are the six stages of making macaroni cheese?

1 ....

2 ....

3 ....

4 ....

5 ....

6 ....   [6]

5 How does the macaroni cheese sauce become thick and smooth?

....

....

....

[5]

Total Marks .... / 19

1 Tick (✓) **one** answer. The main function of fat in pastry is:

    a) to combine other ingredients. ☐   **b)** to shorten the texture. ☐

    c) to spread easily. ☐   **d)** to add bulk to the mix. ☐   [1]

2 This question is about understanding emulsified sauces.

> Basic recipe for Hollandaise sauce:
>
> 250 ml white wine vinegar
>
> 2 egg yolks
>
> 100 g melted butter
>
> Seasoning

    a) Which **two** ingredients would not mix easily?

    .... [2]

    b) What is the function of the seasoning? What might the seasoning be?

    ....

    .... [2]

    c) Explain the function of the egg yolk in the sauce.

    ....

    ....

    .... [3]

3 This question is about function of ingredients in pastry made with half fat to flour.

Choose the correct words from the boxes to complete the following sentences.

steam	dextrinisation	gluten	binds	shorten

    a) Water .... the ingredients together.   [1]

    b) When pastry is cooked .... of starch gives colour.   [1]

    c) Fat is used to .... pastry.   [1]

    d) Water creates .... to help pastry rise.   [1]

    e) Rubbing in fat stops the development of long strands of ....   [1]

Total Marks .... / 13

1. Why is water an effective raising agent? Tick (✓) **one** answer.

   a) It turns to steam. ☐

   b) It does not add calories. ☐

   c) It makes mixtures runny. ☐

   d) It makes mixtures moist. ☐ [1]

2. Fill in the table by naming **two** chemical raising agents and giving an example of their use in food preparation.

Names of Chemical Raising Agent	Example of Use
[1]	[1]
[1]	[1]

3. Name the gas produced by chemical raising agents.

   .... [1]

4. This question is about the function of ingredients in choux pastry.

   a) When making choux paste, state **two** ingredients that help the pastry rise and puff.

   ....   [2]

   b) Explain how these ingredients work during baking.

   ....

   ....

   .... [3]

   c) Why is it important to fully cook small choux buns, e.g. profiteroles?

   ....

   ....

   .... [3]

5. Tick (✓) the correct answer. Raising agents can be classified as:

   a) biological, microbial and physical. ☐

   b) chemical, enzymic and biological. ☐

   c) physical, globular and pathogenic. ☐

   d) chemical, physical and biological. ☐ [1]

Total Marks .... / 15

Microorganisms, Enzymes and Food Spoilage

1. Identify the conditions that food spoilage organisms need to grow.

   ....

   ....

   .... [3]

2. What are the different signs of food spoilage?

   ....

   ....

   .... [3]

3. Suggest **two** ways to store dry food such as flour in order to prevent it from spoiling.

   ....

   ....

   .... [2]

4. Circle the correct option in each of the following sentences.

   a) Moulds grow into a(n) **visible / invisible** plant. [1]

   b) Moulds like **alkali / acid** conditions. [1]

   c) Moulds are destroyed at temperatures above **50 °C / 70 °C**. [1]

   d) Moulds **can / can't** survive in the refrigerator. [1]

   e) Moulds **can / can't** survive in a freezer. [1]

5. Tick (✓) **one** answer. Bacteria grow best at a pH level of: [1]

   a) between 1.6 and 4.5 ☐

   b) between 6.6 and 7.5 ☐

   c) between 3.5 and 8.5 ☐

   d) between 8 and 9 ☐ [1]

   Total Marks .... / 15

Microorganisms in Food Production

1 Choose the correct words from the options given below to complete the text that follows.

| probiotic | harmful | digestion | single | rapidly |

| cheese | food poisoning |

Bacteria are _____ – celled organisms that are able to reproduce _____. Some are _____ and cause _____ or even death. Some bacteria are harmless and are used in _____ making. _____ bacteria help _____. [7]

2 The process of fermentation is used in the production of which food product? Tick (✓) **one** answer.

a) Bread ☐   b) Cheese ☐

c) Yogurt ☐   d) Biscuits ☐   [1]

3 Tick (✓) **one** answer. When producing blue cheese, it is treated with:

a) a starter culture. ☐

b) bacteria. ☐

c) mould. ☐

d) brine. ☐   [1]

4 Explain how yeast makes bread rise.

[3]

Total Marks _____ / 12

1 Complete this table relating to food poisoning.

Name of Bacteria	One Food Source	One Way to Prevent Food Poisoning
a) Salmonella	[1]	[1]
b) Campylobacter	[1]	[1]
c) Bacillus Cereus	[1]	[1]

2 Name **one** symptom of food poisoning.

[1]

3 State **two** conditions that bacteria need in order to reproduce.

[2]

Total Marks _____ / 9

Buying and Storing Food

1 Sally's mother often shops for food during her lunch break.

Describe how she can ensure her food shopping remains at a safe temperature and in good condition until she gets home.

....

....

....

....

....

....

....

....

....

[6]

2 Explain the food hygiene rules that should be followed when storing, preparing and cooking meat.

....

....

....

....

....

....

....

....

....

[6]

Total Marks .... / 12

1 Explain how to reduce the risk of food poisoning when preparing, cooking and storing food in the home.

....

....

....

....

....

....

....

....

[6]

2 State **four** food hygiene rules to be followed when preparing and cooking high-risk foods.

....

....

....

[4]

3 List the hygiene and safety rules you would follow when preparing and cooking food.

....

....

....

....

....

....

....

[8]

Total Marks .... / 18

Food Choices

1 Tick (✓) the boxes below to show if each statement is **True** or **False**.

Statement	True	False
Vegetarians eat fish.		
Buddhists eat pork.		
Sikhs don't eat beef.		

[3]

2 Which part of the body produces insulin? Tick (✓) **one** answer.

a) Stomach ☐   **b)** Liver ☐   **c)** Pancreas ☐   **d)** Spleen ☐   [1]

3 Coeliac disease is caused by the body's immune system reacting to:

a) sucrose. ☐   **b)** thiamin. ☐   **c)** gluten. ☐   **d)** collagen. ☐   [1]

4 State **three** reasons why a person may be a vegetarian.

....

....

....
[3]

5 Explain the difference between a lacto-vegetarian and a vegan in terms of the foods that each does not eat. Explain why each diet differs.

a) Lacto-vegetarian diet

....

....

....

....
[3]

b) Vegan diet

....

....

....

....
[3]

Total Marks .... / 14

1 Tick (✓) **one** answer. 'Cuisine' relates to:

a) the way in which food is cooked in a kitchen. ☐

b) the range of dishes and foods of a particular country or region. ☐

c) the information listed on a food label. ☐ [1]

2 Which of the following is the name of a British cheese? Circle **one** answer.

Gouda   **Wensleydale**   **Brie**   [1]

3 Traditional dishes and foods are important in any society as they originate from the foods grown in that country or region, the local climate and local traditions.

Write the foods in the boxes below next to the correct countries in the table.

| tortilla | Cornish pasty | dhal | minestrone | bouillabaisse | hot pot |

| focaccia | Peking duck | paella | Quiche Lorraine | chow mein | pakora |

Country	Dishes	
a) England		[2]
b) France		[2]
c) Spain		[2]
d) China		[2]
e) India		[2]
f) Italy		[2]

4 Select the cuisine of a country you have studied and complete the table below.

Country Name	Cuisine		
Three main meal dishes	[1]	[1]	[1]
Three vegetables found in recipes	[1]	[1]	[1]

Total Marks _____ / 20

Factors Affecting Food Choice

Sensory Evaluation

1 Which of the following words is another name for aroma? Circle the correct answer.

feel   smell   touch   taste   [1]

2 How many samples of food would be needed to carry out a 'paired preference test'?
Tick (✓) **one** answer.

a) Two ☐

b) Three ☐

c) Four ☐

d) Five ☐   [1]

3 a) Describe how to set up a tasting area to trial your practical work in the food room.

_____

_____

_____

_____

_____

_____

_____ [6]

b) What do you understand by a triangle test?

_____

_____

_____ [4]

c) Give **one** example of how you could carry out triangle testing when developing healthier recipes using minced beef.

Name of product: _____ [1]

Samples to trial: _____

_____ [2]

Total Marks _____ / 15

Food Labelling

1 Which food label indicates that the food should no longer be offered for sale in a shop? Tick (✓) **one** answer.

a) Use by ☐   b) Display until ☐

c) Sell by ☐   d) Best by ☐   [1]

2 Which of the following foods is **not** classed as an allergen? Tick (✓) **one** answer.

a) Mustard ☐   b) Pumpkin seeds ☐

c) Celery ☐   d) Peanuts ☐   [1]

3 a) What does GDA stand for?

.... [1]

b) How is GDA displayed on the front of a product label?

....
....
.... [3]

c) Legally, the name of the product must be printed on food packaging. Explain six other items of information that also must be given by law.

....
....
....
....
....
.... [6]

4 Which of the following items does **not** need to be included on a nutrition label on pre-packed foods? Tick (✓) **one** answer.

a) Protein ☐   b) Carbohydrate ☐

c) Salt ☐   d) Sugars ☐   [1]

Total Marks .... / 13

Factors Affecting Food Choice

1 In which of these months are British strawberries at their best? Tick (✓) **one** answer.

a) May/June ☐   b) June/July ☐

c) July/August ☐   d) August/September ☐   [1]

2 Tick (✓) **one** answer. The best strategy to eat a healthy and varied diet is to:

a) buy what is on offer. ☐

b) make a shopping list. ☐

c) plan a shopping diary, make a shopping list, and keep to it. ☐

d) eat lots of fruit and vegetables. ☐   [1]

3 a) Explain the benefits for young people of being active for at least 60 minutes every day.

....

....

....

....   [4]

b) To maintain a healthy weight, what eating model does the UK Government suggest that people use?

....   [1]

c) What factors will make a meal more enjoyable to eat?

....

....

....   [3]

d) Explain **four** factors that affect the eating patterns within a household.

....

....

....

....

....

....   [4]

Total Marks .... / 14

1 Choose the correct words from the boxes below to complete the following sentences.

| transport | process | dispose | energy | carbon footprint | carbon dioxide |

At each stage of a product's lifecycle .... is needed to

...., ... and .... of the product;

.... is produced as a byproduct of energy use. The .... is

the calculation of the carbon dioxide produced throughout a product's life. [6]

2 Choose the correct words from the boxes below to complete the following sentences.

| livestock | soil erosion | pasture | wasteland | plantations | deforestation |

.... occurs when trees are cut down. Cleared land is used as

.... for .... and .... of commodities

and settlements. Deforested regions typically suffer .... and frequently

degrade into .... [6]

3 When you throw away food, you waste not only the food but also the resources, such as energy, fuel and water, that went into growing, harvesting, transporting and storing the food. Discarded food then goes on to produce methane in landfill sites. Explain what every person can do to prevent this food waste.

....

....

....

....

....

....

....

[6]

4 Name **two** dishes that make use of leftover food.

....

[2]

Total Marks .... / 20

Food Provenance and Production Methods

1 Why is traceability important?

....

....

....

....

....

....

.... [4]

2 Explain the differences between the hens that lay battery, free range, barn and organic eggs.

Battery ....

.... [2]

Free-range ....

.... [2]

Barn ....

.... [2]

Organic ....

.... [2]

3 What concerns are there about GM (Genetically Modified) food production? Tick (✓) the correct answers.

a) It is more expensive.   ☐

b) There is a possibility of new strains of microorganisms developing.   ☐

c) It is altering and playing with nature.   ☐

d) It is less resistant to plant disease.   ☐

e) It is not monitored.   ☐   [2]

Total Marks .... / 14

1 If large areas of rainforest are cut down, which gas will build up?

.... [1]

2 Write about **three** different things that can be done to tackle the sustainability of a food source.

....

....

.... [3]

3

FAIRTRADE

a) What does this logo mean?

....

.... [2]

b) Give **two** examples of foods that could display this logo.

.... [1]

4 What are the advantages of buying a pack of chicken that displays the Red Tractor logo?

....

....

....

....

....

....

.... [8]

5 Beef burgers are a very popular takeaway food and use beef, which means that more cattle are reared to supply the fast food industry. Explain what effect this demand for beef supply is having on our climate.

....

....

.... [2]

Total Marks .... / 17

1   What is homogenised milk?

_____

_____ [2]

2   What can happen if cream is heated?

_____ [1]

3   a)   Name **three** regional varieties of cheese from the UK.

_____ [3]

    b)   Name **three** French cheeses.

_____ [3]

4   Name **six** different types of flour made from wheat.

_____

_____ [6]

5   Choose the correct words from the boxes to complete the following sentences.

gluten	sugar	yeast	proving	kneading	glaze	dough	liquid

Bread is made by mixing strong flour (which is high in _____) with

_____ and a raising agent such as _____. The yeast ferments

with _____ and warm water, and then when added to the flour and salt it makes

a _____. The dough is then worked by a process called _____.

The dough is then allowed to rise further by standing covered in a warm environment.

This is known as _____. The bread dough is then shaped and finished with a

_____ before baking.   [8]

6   What type of flour is used to make pasta? What is it made from?

_____ [2]

Total Marks _____ / 25

1 Name the **four** main types of food preservation.

[4]

2 You have been growing your own fruit and have a large crop of apples. How can you preserve them? Explain your method, and the shelf life of your chosen method.

Method

Shelf life

[2]

3 What is the main advantage of low-temperature storage when considering the nutritional value of food?

[1]

4 Often meats or fish are 'smoked'. What does this mean?

[2]

5 Years ago, before electricity, there were no fridges and freezers, so how did people preserve the produce from gardens to last through the seasons?

[4]

6 Roll mops are a traditional fish dish. What method of preservation do they use?

[1]

7 How is bacon preserved?

[2]

Total Marks _____ / 16

Collins

GCSE
Food Preparation
And Nutrition
Practice Paper 1

Materials

Time allowed: 1 hour 45 minutes

For this paper you must have:

- a black pen
- a pencil.

Instructions

- Use black ink or black ball-point pen.
- Answer **all** questions.
- You must answer the questions in the spaces provided. Do not write outside the box around each page or on blank pages.
- Do all rough work in this answer book. Cross through any work you do not want to be marked.

Information

- The marks for questions are shown in brackets.
- The maximum mark for this paper is 100.
- You are reminded of the need for good English and clear presentation in your answers.

Name: ....

Practice Exam Paper 1

Section A consists of multiple choice questions.

There are 20 marks available.
Answer all questions.

For each question you should shade in **one** box.

An example is shown below.

Which food is high in fat?

A Bread ☐

B Cheese ■

C Broccoli ☐

D Apple ☐

Question 1 is about diet, nutrition and health.

0 1 · 1 Fats are made up of which **two** components?

A Cholesterol and acetic acid ☐

B Fatty acids and glycerol ☐

C Glycerol and glucose ☐

D Butter and margarine ☐   [1 mark]

0 1 · 2 Plants manufacture carbohydrate by a process known as:

A osmosis. ☐

B osteoporosis. ☐

C combustion. ☐

D photosynthesis. ☐   [1 mark]

0 1 · 3 A deficiency of iron in the diet can cause anaemia. Which of the following foods is a dietary source of iron?

A Olive oil ☐

B Soda bread ☐

C Liver ☐

D Cottage cheese ☐ [1 mark]

0 1 · 4 Coronary Heart Disease is caused by a build-up of what substance in the arteries?

A Cholesterol ☐

B Bile ☐

C Riboflavin ☐

D Glycerol ☐ [1 mark]

Question 2 is about food safety.

0 2 · 1 After which **one** of the following activities is it most important for the food handler to wash their hands?

A Washing lettuce ☐

B Spreading butter on bread ☐

C Peeling fruit ☐

D Preparing raw chicken ☐ [1 mark]

0 2 · 2 Which of the following is most likely to cause cross contamination?

A Using ready-to-eat foods within their use-by date ☐

B Placing ready-to-eat foods above raw foods in a fridge ☐

C Using the same knife to cut raw chicken and cooked ham ☐

D Storing raw chicken in a covered container at the bottom of the fridge ☐ [1 mark]

0 2 · 3 What is the temperature regarded as the danger zone?

A 0–5 °C

B 0–63 °C

C 5°C–63 °C

D 5–50 °C [1 mark]

0 2 · 4 Which microorganism is used in the manufacture of bread?

A Yeast

B Flour

C Salt

D Salmonella [1 mark]

Question 3 is about food science.

0 3 · 1 Which **one** of the following is a true statement?

Choux paste is raised by:

A flour as it gelatinises during cooking.

B water as it turns to steam during baking.

C beating during the adding of the flour.

D eggs enriching the choux paste. [1 mark]

0 3 · 2 Which type of flour has the highest chemical raising agent content?

A Self-raising flour

B Soya flour

C Maize flour

D Plain wheat flour [1 mark]

0 3 · 3 Complete this sentence.

The main function of egg in pancake batter is:

A   to gelatinise during cooking. ☐

B   to bind the batter mixture. ☐

C   to set the mixture by coagulating. ☐

D   to brown the mixture by caramelising. ☐ [1 mark]

0 3 · 4 When making whisked sponge, which gas is trapped during whisking?

A   Lecithin ☐

B   Sulphur ☐

C   Air ☐

D   Carbon dioxide ☐ [1 mark]

Question 4 is about food provenance.

0 4 · 1 What is intensive farming?

A   Farmers who work 24 hours a day, seven days a week. ☐

B   Small farms that specialise in rearing just one animal or crop. ☐

C   Large-scale farms that focus on large-scale production of crops
or animals in a short period of time. ☐

D   Farms that have a large variety of animals or crops. ☐ [1 mark]

0 4 · 2 Deforestation contributes to global warming with excesses of which gas?

A CO_2 ☐

B   Methane ☐

C   Carbon monoxide ☐

D   Oxygen ☐ [1 mark]

0 4 · 3 What is hydroponics?

A   An irrigation system for fields ☐

B   Nutrient-rich liquids in which to grow plants ☐

C   Ponds on farms that provide animal drinking water ☐

D   Water drip feeders for hens in barns ☐ [1 mark]

0 4 · 4 When making bread, which type of flour do we need to use?

A   Durum wheat 00 flour ☐

B   Plain flour ☐

C   Strong flour ☐

D   Self-raising flour ☐ [1 mark]

Question 5 is about food choices.

0 5 · 1 If you have Coeliac disease, which **one** of the following foods are you **not** able to eat?

A   Rice ☐

B   Potatoes ☐

C   Bread ☐

D   Cabbage ☐ [1 mark]

0 5 · 2 Which **one** of the following foods does a lacto-vegetarian **include** in their diet?

A   Milk ☐

B   Eggs ☐

C   Fish ☐

D   Meat ☐ [1 mark]

0 5 · 3 Which **one** of these is a **true** definition of a shopping list?

    A List of offers on sale   ☐

    B List of foods to buy   ☐

    C List of dishes to make   ☐

    D List of foods people like   ☐   **[1 mark]**

0 5 · 4 Which term describes how food **feels** in the mouth when eating?

    A Aroma   ☐

    B Taste   ☐

    C Texture   ☐

    D Appearance   ☐   **[1 mark]**

Section B

Answer all questions in this section.
There are 80 marks available.

Question 6 is about diet, nutrition and health.

`0 6 · 1` One of the most common medical procedures for primary school children is dental extraction. Dentists are increasingly concerned that this problem is growing. Explain in detail how sugar can cause tooth decay.

_____

_____

_____

_____

_____

_____

[4 marks]

`0 6 · 2` Suggest four ways in which children's sugar consumption can be reduced.

_____

_____

_____

_____

[4 marks]

0 6 · 3 Name **two** other diseases that can be caused by a high intake of sugar. Discuss how too much sugar causes these diseases.

[6 marks]

0 6 · 4 Sugar is a carbohydrate. Name the **two** other carbohydrate groups and give **two** examples of foods from each.

[6 marks]

0 6 · 5 Consider and explain the nutritional requirements of primary school children, detailing each nutrient group.

....

....

....

....

....

....

....

....

[12 marks]

Question 7 is about cooking food.

The information below shows a recipe for béchamel sauce.

400 ml milk	25 g piece of carrot	1 stalk of celery	6 black peppercorns
1 bay leaf	Seasoning	25 g margarine	25 g flour

Using the information above, answer the following questions.

0 7 · 1 Which herbs and spices are used in this recipe? Give **one** example of each.

Herb ....

Spice ....

[2 marks]

0 7 · 2 Explain why béchamel sauce is not suitable for someone who is lactose intolerant.

[2 marks]

0 7 · 3 Explain how heat is transferred when the vegetables and peppercorns are infused in the milk.

[3 marks]

0 7 · 4 Explain how the liquid is thickened by the roux.

[3 marks]

0 7 · 5 The table below shows **two** dishes that use flour as an ingredient. For each dish give **one** function of the flour and **one** description of the function.

Name of Dish	Function	Description
Choux pastry		
Bread		

[6 marks]

Question 8 is about food provenance.

0 8 · 1 Fresh milk is processed into several different types of milk. Name **four** different varieties of milk and explain how they are different from each other, e.g. in homogenised milk the fat is broken up and dispersed through the milk so it doesn't reform as a layer.

....

....

....

....

....

....

[8 marks]

0 8 . 2 Secondary processing of milk produces a whole variety of milk-based products.
Name **two** milk-based products and describe how they are made.

....

....

....

....

....

....

[6 marks]

Question 9 is about understanding recipes.

Information about two pasta sauces is given below.

Information about nutrients

Ingredients in quantity order	Ingredients	energy kcal	protein g	carbohydrate g	unsaturated fat g	saturated fat g	dietary fibre g	sugar g	salt g
Sauce A Tomato sauce with black olives, aubergine and ricotta	tomatoes aubergine olive oil black olives ricotta onion oregano	148 kcal	3.2 g	7 g	9.8 g	2.2 g	4 g	3.2 g	1.9 g
Sauce B Chorizo and chilli sauce	tomatoes onion red pepper chorizo olive oil smoked paprika black pepper lemon juice	66 kcal	1.7 g	7.2 g	3 g	0.7 g	1 g	4.8 g	0.5 g

`0 9` · `1` With reference to the ingredients and nutrient content of each of the sauces, evaluate the suitability of these sauces for obese people.

Give reasons for your choices.

....

....

....

....

....

....

[8 marks]

Question 10 is about food preparation and food safety.

| 1 0 · 1 | The table below shows some problems seen when food is prepared. Complete the table to show **two** different causes of each problem.

Problem	Causes
Victoria sandwich not rising	Cause 1
	Cause 2
Lumpy cheese sauce	Cause 1
	Cause 2

[4 marks]

10 . 2 'High-risk foods are most likely to cause food poisoning.' Explain this statement.

_____

_____

_____

_____

_____

_____

_____

_____

_____

_____

[6 marks]

END OF QUESTIONS

Collins

GCSE
Food Preparation And Nutrition
Practice Paper 2

Materials   Time allowed: 1 hour 45 minutes

For this paper you must have:

- a black pen
- a pencil.

Instructions

- Use black ink or black ball-point pen.
- Answer **all** questions.
- You must answer the questions in the spaces provided. Do not write outside the box around each page or on blank pages.
- Do all rough work in this answer book. Cross through any work you do not want to be marked.

Information

- The marks for questions are shown in brackets.
- The maximum mark for this paper is 100.
- You are reminded of the need for good English and clear presentation in your answers.

Name: ....

Section A consists of multiple choice questions.

There are 20 marks available.
Answer all questions.

For each question you should shade in **one** box.

An example is shown below.

Which food is high in fat?

A Bread ☐

B Cheese ■

C Broccoli ☐

D Apple ☐

Question 1 **is about diet, nutrition and health.**

`0 1 · 1` A person who is unable to eat wheat products is:

A vegan. ☐

B coeliac. ☐

C diabetic. ☐

D anaemic. ☐ **[1 mark]**

`0 1 · 2` Citrus fruits are a good source of:

A iron. ☐

B calcium. ☐

C vitamin D. ☐

D vitamin C. ☐ **[1 mark]**

Practice Exam Paper 2

0 1 · 3 Which of the following is not a function of vitamins?

A   Prevent illness and maintain good health ☐

B   Protect the body's internal organs ☐

C   Aid building and repair in the body ☐

D   Control the release of energy by the body ☐   [1 mark]

0 1 · 4 Which of the following contains a vegetable source of fat?

A   Rapeseed oil ☐

B   Cream ☐

C   Butter ☐

D   Lard ☐   [1 mark]

Question 2 is about food safety.

0 2 · 1 Which food poisoning bacteria are commonly found on human skin?

A   Clostridium botulinum ☐

B   Salmonella enteritidis ☐

C   Staphylococcus aureus ☐

D   Clostridium perfringens ☐   [1 mark]

0 2 · 2 Which of the following does bacteria need in order to multiply?

A   Light ☐

B   Moisture ☐

C   Sugar ☐

D   Salt ☐   [1 mark]

0 2 · 3 What is the required temperature for fridge storage?

    A 1–4 °C (below 5 °C) ☐

    B 5–15 °C (below 15 °C) ☐

    C 0–63 °C ☐

    D Minus 15 °C ☐ [1 mark]

0 2 · 4 Why are use-by dates put on high-risk foods?

    A This is the date that the food will be at its best to eat. ☐

    B The food is perishable and may be unsafe to eat after that date. ☐

    C So that the food is not eaten by high-risk groups. ☐

    D So that you know when to put the item in the freezer. ☐ [1 mark]

Question 3 is about food science.

0 3 · 1 Which **one** of the following is a true statement?
Food is cooked to:

    A make it safe to eat and give variety in the diet. ☐

    B incorporate carbohydrates, fats and proteins. ☐

    C soften food and prevent lumps from forming. ☐

    D make it suitable to eat immediately after cooking. ☐ [1 mark]

0 3 · 2 Which type of cooking method uses the most water?

    A Stir frying ☐

    B Braising ☐

    C Steaming ☐

    D Boiling ☐ [1 mark]

0 3 · 3 Complete this sentence.

The main function of grilling sliced bread is:

A caramelisation of the surface. ☐

B dextrinisation of the starch. ☐

C coagulation of the gluten. ☐

D gelatinisation of the starch. ☐ [1 mark]

0 3 · 4 When cooking in an oven, which main heat transfer is used?

A Radiation ☐

B Microwave ☐

C Conduction ☐

D Convection ☐ [1 mark]

Question 4 is about food provenance.

0 4 · 1 4.1 What does MAP stand for? ☐

A Made Abroad Product ☐

B Modified Atmospheric Packaging ☐

C Microwavable Appetising Product ☐

D Modified Additive Product ☐ [1 mark]

0 4 · 2 Often when purchasing fish, the packaging says 'from sustainable sources'. What does this mean?

A The fish have been caught whilst young so they are more tender. ☐

B The holes in the fishing nets are small to ensure that no fish get away. ☐

C Fish are caught by fisherman observing fish quotas. ☐

D The fish have been processed and chilled on the ship after being caught. ☐ [1 mark]

0 4 · 3 Which of the following does not contribute to global warming?

    A Most households owning and using refrigerators ☐

    B Recycling of packaging ☐

    C Food production and transporting products ☐

    D Home-grown fruit and vegetables ☐   **[1 mark]**

0 4 · 4 One of the effects of climate change can be flooding. Which of the following is not a consequence of this?

    A Livestock drowned ☐

    B Land polluted by sewage and debris ☐

    C Pests invading crops and destroying them ☐

    D Soil and nutrients are washed away ☐   **[1 mark]**

Question 5 is about food choices.

0 5 · 1 Which sensory test finds out how much someone likes the taste of a food?

    A Triangle ☐

    B Ranking ☐

    C Rating ☐

    D Paired preference ☐   **[1 mark]**

0 5 · 2 Which food is traditionally eaten at Jewish Passover?

    A Unleavened bread ☐

    B Baklava ☐

    C Hot cross buns ☐

    D Pumpkin pie ☐   **[1 mark]**

0 5 · 3 Which of the following foods is **not** one of the 14 allergen foods?

A Soybeans ☐

B Crustaceans ☐

C Beetroot ☐

D Cow's milk ☐ [1 mark]

0 5 · 4 Which of these ingredients is likely to be the **least** expensive when shopping for food on a budget?

A Fish ☐

B Strawberries ☐

C Asparagus ☐

D Potatoes ☐ [1 mark]

Section B

Answer all questions in this section.
There are 80 marks available.

Question 6 is about diet, nutrition and health.

0 6 · 1 Diets which are high in saturated fats are directly linked to several serious health problems.

> Sam is a teenager. He has a fried breakfast every day: two economy sausages, streaky bacon rashers, fried egg and fried wholemeal bread with a hot chocolate drink made with whole milk.

Explain how the macronutrient content of the breakfast provides Sam with energy.

[6 marks]

0 6 · 2 In the UK diets high in saturated fats are directly linked to several serious health problems.

Assess the various factors that contribute to high fat intake and explain how high fat diets in childhood and teenage years may put future health at risk.

....

....

....

....

....

....

....

....

....

....

....

[12 marks]

0 6 · 3 Describe and explain **three** functions of fat in the body.

....

....

....

....

....

....

[6 marks]

0 6 . 4 Fat and oils have different chemical compositions.

Describe the different make-up of the following types of fat, giving **two** examples of each type.

Saturated

....

....

....

....

....

Unsaturated

....

....

....

....

....

[8 marks]

Question 7 is about cooking food.

The information below shows a recipe for shortbread.

150 g plain four	100 g butter	50 g caster sugar
Grated lemon zest	Ground cinnamon	

Using the information above, answer the following questions.

`0 7 · 1` Which flavouring and which spice is used in the recipe?

Flavouring ....

Spice ....

[2 marks]

`0 7 · 2` Explain why this recipe is not suitable for someone who needs to reduce saturates in their diet.

....

....

....

[2 marks]

`0 7 · 3` Explain how heat is transferred during cooking the shortbread.

....

....

....

[3 marks]

0 7 · 4 Explain the changes that occur during baking the shortbread.

_____

_____

_____

[3 marks]

0 7 · 5 The table below shows **two** dishes that use margarine as an ingredient. For each dish give **one** function of the margarine and **one** description of the function.

Name of Dish	Function	Description
Pastry tarts		
Sponge cake		

[6 marks]

Question 8 is about food provenance.

0 8 · 1 Farmers' markets are very popular these days. Discuss the advantages of buying from farmers' markets.

_____

[6 marks]

0 8 . 2 Many farmers' markets sell fresh farm eggs, but these can be laid by hens in a variety of housing conditions. Describe **three** different ways of egg farming.

[6 marks]

0 8 . 3 How you can ensure you are buying a quality product when buying fresh eggs?

[2 marks]

Question 9 is about understanding recipes.

Information about two gluten-free sausages is given below.

Nutrients per 100 g

Ingredients in quantity order	Ingredients	energy kcal	protein g	carbohydrate g	unsaturated fat g	saturated fat g	dietary fibre g	sugar g	salt g
Sausage A Quorn Gluten-free	Quorn onion rice flour potato starch egg white black pepper thyme sage	197 kcal	15.7 g	10.3 g	8.3 g	0.8 g	5.5 g	1 g	1.2 g
Sausage B Musks Gluten-free	pork rice salt spices	210 kcal	15.0 g	3.5 g	9.2 g	5.5 g	0.7 g	0.7 g	1.8 g

0 9. 1 With reference to the ingredients and nutrient content of each of the sausages, evaluate the suitability of these sausages for a person who is coeliac.

Give reasons for your choice.

....

....

....

....

....

....

....

....

....

[8 marks]

Question 10 is about food preparation and food safety.

1 0 · 1 The table below shows some problems seen when food is prepared.

Complete the table to show **two** different causes of each problem.

Problem	Causes
Bread not rising	Cause 1
	Cause 2
Quiche not setting	Cause 1
	Cause 2

[4 marks]

Practice Exam Paper 2

1 0 . 2 Explain how you can prevent food poisoning when storing food in the home.

_____

_____

_____

_____

_____

_____

_____

_____

_____

_____

[6 marks]

END OF QUESTIONS

Answers

Page 4: Knife Skills

1. a) [1]
2. b) [1]
3. Name of knife hold 1: Bridge hold [1]
   Explanation: Form a bridge with thumb and index finger, hold item flat side down on chopping board, position knife under the bridge and cut firmly downwards. [1]
   Name of knife hold 2: Claw grip [1]
   Explanation: Place item to be cut flat side down on chopping board, shape hand into a claw, tuck thumb inside fingers, rest the claw on item to be sliced, use other hand to slice the item, moving clawed fingers away as cutting progresses. [1]
4. **Any four from:** Carry knife pointing downwards [1]; Handle should be grease-free [1]; Don't put in washing-up bowl [1]; Keep clean [1]; Keep sharp [1]; Do not leave on edge of surface [1]; Use correct knife for the job to be done [1].

Page 5: Fish

1. c) [1]
2. a) [1]
3. d) [1]
4. Enrobing [1]; Coating [1]
5. Fish cooks quickly because the muscle [1] is short and the connective tissue [1] is thin.
   The connective tissue is made up of collagen [1] and will change into gelatine [1] and coagulate [1] at 60 °C [1].
6. Classification of fish: round
   One example of fish: **any one of:** Cod [1]; Haddock [1]; Whiting [1]; Pollock [1]; Coley [1].
   Chef is cutting into the top of the fish on one side of the tail to detach the backbone from the head to the tail [1]; Chef has left the head on the fish [1].

Page 6: Meat

1. d) [1]
2. c) [1]
3. Meat is a muscle [1] composed of cells consisting of fibres [1], held together by connective tissue [1].
4. **Any one of:** Leg [1]; Shoulder [1].
5. **Any two from:** Stewing [1]; Braising [1]; Casserole [1]; Pot-roasting [1].
6. The browning [1] of meat is caused by a reaction with natural sugars [1] and proteins to produce a dark colour. This occurrence is called the Maillard [1] reaction or non-enzymic browning. As the meat cooks the proteins coagulate [1] and produce a firm texture. Collagen is broken down into gelatine [1].

Page 7: Prepare, Combine and Shape

1. c) [1]
2. a) [1]
3. Whisking involves adding air into the mixture while mixing [1]; Stirring does not involve adding air into the mixture while mixing [1].
4. **Any two from:** Consistency of depth [1]; Consistency of size [1]; Consistency of shape [1].
5. The following mixing skills should be used to ensure the smooth consistency of the batter: Cream [1] together the fat and sugar [1]; Beat [1] the eggs; Fold [1] in the flour. The following shaping skills should be used to ensure quality of finish: Use cake tins [1] to mould [1] the shape of the cake; Pipe [1] the cream for a good decorative finish [1].
6. Use a burger mould (or burger press) [1]; Weigh the mixture to make sure the same quantity is used for each burger [1]

Page 8: Dough

1. c) [1]
2. b) [1]
3. Rubbing in [1]
4. To bind the dough together [1]
5. Weigh all the ingredients accurately [1].
   Place fat [1] and water [1] in a pan and bring to a rolling boil [1].
   Add sieved flour [1] immediately and mix well to form a paste [1].
   Cool [1] then add beaten eggs gradually to a heavy dropping [1] consistency. Cook in a hot oven.
6. Glutenin [1]; Gliadin [1]

Page 9: Protein and Fat

1. growth [1]; repair [1]
2. Possible answers, **any two from:** Cheese [1]; Milk [1]; Eggs [1]; Pulse vegetables [1]; Soya [1]; TVP [1]; Mycoprotein (Quorn) [1]; Nuts [1]
3. Possible answers, **any three from:** Meat [1]; Fish [1]; Cheese [1]; Eggs [1]; Milk [1]; Soya [1].
4. Lentil soup and bread [1]
5. c) [1]
6. Possible answers, **any one of:** Any type of oil, e.g. groundnut oil [1]; Vegetable oil [1]; Olive oil [1]; Sunflower oil [1]; Any solid fat that has been melted [1].
7. Provides concentrated energy. [1]; Provides body with vitamins A, D, E and K. [1]
8. Fatty Acids [1]; Glycerol [1]
9. Hydrogenation is the name given to the process that makes solid fat from a liquid oil [1].

Page 10: Carbohydrate

1. Sugars [1]; Starches [1]; Non-Starch Polysaccharide (dietary fibre) [1]
2. Possible answers, **any one of:** Glucose [1]; Galactose [1]; Fructose [1].
3. digested [1]; energy [1]
4. a) **Any one of:** Wholemeal bread [1]; Granary bread [1].
   b) **Any one of:** Branflakes [1]; All Bran [1]; Fruit and fibre, etc. [1].
   c) Jacket potatoes [1]
5. Dental decay [1]
6. **Any two from:** The body will start to use protein and fat as an energy source [1]; Weight loss [1]; Lack of energy [1]; Poor digestive health [1].
7. Starches [1] have to be digested into sugars [1] before absorption [1] – this is slow energy release [1].
8. Constipation [1]

Page 11: Vitamins

1. Possible answers, **any two from:** Liver [1]; Whole milk [1]; Cheese [1]; Green leafy vegetables [1]; Carrots [1].
2. The water soluble group of vitamins [1]
3. Weak bones in children, that bend under body weight [1]; Associated with a vitamin D deficiency [1]
4. Skin cracking around the mouth [1]
5. Antioxidants protect us from pollutants in the environment [1].
6. A type of vitamin D [1] formed by action of sunlight on the skin [1]
7. When making a salad, to avoid the loss of vitamin C (ascorbic acid [1]) through oxidation [1], prepare just before serving [1] and avoid excess cutting [1].
8. b) [1]

Page 12: Minerals and Water

1. d) [1]
2. **Any one of:** Strong bones [1]; Strong teeth [1]; To enable clotting of blood [1]; For nerves and muscles [1]; Works with Vitamin D [1]; Prevents rickets/brittle bones/osteoporosis [1].
3. **Any one of:** High blood pressure [1]; Heart disease [1]; Strokes [1].
4. Flavour [1]
5. A lack of iron in the diet can cause iron deficiency anaemia [1] and symptoms include tiredness [1].
6. Between six and eight glasses [1]
7. Fluoride is important for strengthening teeth against decay [1]
8. a) [1]

Page 13: Making Informed Choices

1. Fruit and vegetables [1]; Potatoes, bread, rice, pasta and other starchy carbohydrates [1]; Beans, pulses, fish, eggs, meat and other proteins [1];

Dairy (and alternatives) [1]; Oils and Spreads [1]

2. Human milk [1] provides babies with all their nutritional requirements, except for iron [1]. Babies are born with a supply of this stored in their liver [1].
3. A mother's first milk is called colostrum and it is full of antibodies [1].
4. For the development of the neural tube of the foetus [1]. This can prevent the condition spina bifida [1].
5. c) [1]
6. The Eatwell Guide [1] shows the proportions of food groups that should be eaten daily for a well-balanced [1] diet.
7. Eat plenty of fibre-rich foods [1]; for example, **any one of**: wholegrain cereals/wholemeal bread/wholegrain breakfast cereals/wholemeal pasta/wholemeal flour/fruit/ vegetables/ dried fruit/nuts/seeds/ beans, peas/lentils [1].

Page 14: Diet, Nutrition and Health

1. Coronary Heart Disease [1] is linked to diets high in saturated fats [1], which make cholesterol [1] in the blood.
2. c) [1]
3. Five to seven portions (allow 5 portions) [1]
4. **Any three from**: Weight gain/obesity [1]; Can produce high/bad cholesterol [1]; Can block arteries [1]; Angina [1]; Coronary Heart Disease (CHD)/ heart disease/heart attack [1]; Higher consumption of trans fats/higher risk of cancer [1].
5. In Type 2 diabetes, too little or no insulin [1] is produced resulting in high levels of sugar [1] in the blood [1].
6. b) [1]
7. Age [1]; Gender [1]; Body size [1]

Page 15: Cooking of Food, Heat Transfer and Selecting Appropriate Cooking Methods

1. c) [1]
2. Cooking uses heat [1]; in order to change the texture, flavour and colour of food [1]; and to improve palatability [1].
3. Dry method, change to nutritional content: Reduces fat [1]; Example: Grilling sausages.
Water-based method, change to nutritional content: (moist method) vitamin C loss [1]; Example: Boiling potatoes/cabbage [1].
4. Cooking methods can alter the sensory [1] properties of food by adding crispness or softening.
The right cooking methods can conserve [1] vitamins, or add [1] energy value.
When meat needs cooking, long, slow moist [1] cooking is best for tough [1] cuts of meat.
If the meat is tender a quick [1] and hot [1] method of cooking such as grilling can be used.

Page 16: Proteins and Enzymic Browning

1. c) [1]
2. a) A marinade is a liquid [1]; made from flavoursome and acidic ingredients that is used to soak [1]; foods prior [1] to cooking.
b) A marinade is used to add flavour to foods from ingredients such as garlic, chillies, herbs and/or spices [1]; A marinade using acidic ingredients such as lemon juice, vinegar or buttermilk is used to make ingredients such as meat or fish more tender [1]; Marinades help to add moistness in foods that otherwise might be dry [1].
c) Chicken has a fairly bland, mild flavour [1]; therefore a marinade would add flavour [1]; The meat, chicken, would be made tender, kept juicy and not be tough [1]; and would cook quickly [1]
d) BBQ [1]; Grill [1]
3. a) True [1]
b) True [1]
c) False [1]
d) True [1]

Page 17: Carbohydrates

1. a) [1]
2. b) [1]
3. semi-skimmed milk: liquid for the sauce [1]
wheat flour: thickener [1]
margarine: fat for the roux [1]
seasoning: salt and pepper flavour [1]
Red Leicester cheese: main protein/ cheese flavour [1]
macaroni: pasta/carbohydrate [1]
4. 1 Boil the pasta [1]
2 Drain the pasta [1]
3 Prepare the sauce [1]
4 Use the roux method or use the all-in-one method to prepare the sauce [1]
5 Assemble the pasta and the sauce [1]
6 Au gratin option [1]
5. Mix the roux (or use the all-in-one method) [1]; Heat thickens by starch gelatinising [2]; and beat – agitation ensures smoothness [2]

Page 18: Fats and Oils

1. b) [1]
2. a) The vinegar [1]; and the melted butter [1] would not mix easily – they would separate on standing
b) Seasoning makes the sauce taste better [1]; Salt and pepper are commonly used as seasoning [1]
c) The egg yolk contains lecithin [1]; which emulsifies [1]; the butter and vinegar to create a stable sauce [1]
3. a) binds [1]
b) dextrinisation [1]
c) shorten [1]
d) steam [1]
e) gluten [1]

Page 19: Raising Agents

1. a) [1]
2. Names of chemical raising agents: Bicarbonate of soda [1]; Baking powder [1]
Examples of use, **any two of**: Scones [1]; Gingerbread [1]; Biscuits [1].
3. Carbon dioxide [1]
4. a) Water [1]; Eggs [1]
b) During baking the water turns to steam [1]; The eggs expand [1]; Before setting/coagulating [1], holding the risen shape
c) Fully cooked buns are dry inside [1]; Steam has escaped [1]; This prevents collapse [1]
5. d) [1]

Page 20: Microorganisms, Enzymes and Food Spoilage

1. **Any three from**: Warm temperature/ 37 °C [1]; Moisture [1]; Food [1]; Time [1]; Neutral pH [1]; May need oxygen [1].
2. **Any three from**: Mould grows [1]; Flavour changes (souring) [1]; Bacterial contamination [1]; Physical contamination from dirty machinery or careless food handlers [1]; Contamination by flies, cockroaches, mice, rats, mites, domestic animals [1]; Contamination by chemicals/radiation/ pollution [1]; Colour changes [1]; Texture changes [1]; Unpleasant odour [1].
3. **Any two from**: Cupboard should be free from vermin and pets [1]; Wash shelves regularly/deal with spills immediately [1]; Make sure storage containers are clean [1]; Do not top up existing stock with new [1]; Store dry foods in airtight containers/ sealed packets [1]; Keep a check on approximate storage times/best before dates [1]; Store in a cool dry place [1].
4. a) visible [1]
b) acid [1]
c) 70 °C [1]
d) can [1]
e) can't [1]
5. b) [1]

Page 21: Microorganisms in Food Production

1. Bacteria are single [1] -celled organisms that are able to reproduce rapidly [1]. Some are harmful [1] and cause food poisoning [1] or even death. Some bacteria are harmless and are used in cheese [1] making. Probiotic [1] bacteria help digestion [1].
2. a) [1]
3. c) [1]
4. Air bubbles are trapped and distributed throughout the bread dough as it is mixed and kneaded [1]; The yeast absorbs the starches and sugars in the flour, turning them into alcohol and carbon dioxide gas

[1]; The gas inflates the air bubbles, causing the bread to rise [1].

Page 22: Bacterial Contamination

1. a) Food source, **any one of**: Raw meat, poultry/chicken [1]; Eggs [1]; Cooked meat [1]; Dairy foods [1]; Cheese [1]; Mayonnaise [1]; Bean sprouts.
        Prevention, **any one of**: Wash hands after handling raw meat, eggs etc. [1]; Hard boil eggs/avoid lightly cooked or raw eggs [1]; Defrost chicken before cooking [1]; Cook meat, poultry/chicken thoroughly [1]; Boil bean sprouts before use.
    b) Food source, **any one of**: Meat [1]; Shellfish [1]; Untreated water [1]; Washing raw poultry [1].
        Prevention, **any one of**: Take measures to prevent transmission between humans [1]; Raw meat and poultry **must not** be washed, as this spreads the bacteria [1].
    c) Food source, **any one of**: Cooked rice [1]; Herbs and spices [1]; Starchy food products [1].
        Prevention, **any one of**: Do not reheat rice dishes [1]; Cool cooked rice immediately after cooking when making salads etc. [1]; Do not keep herbs and spices past use-by date [1].
2. **Any one of**: Diarrhoea [1]; Dehydration [1]; Headache [1]; High/low temperature [1]; Sickness/vomiting [1]; Stomach ache/cramps/nausea/feel sick [1].
3. **Any two from**: Food/nutrients [1]; Moisture/damp [1]; Oxygen/air [1]; Time [1]; Warmth [1].

Page 23: Buying and Storing Food

1. **Any six from**: Use a cool bag/cool box/polystyrene material to insulate the cold food from room temperature [1]; Keep the food covered in the boot of the car, if transporting home by car [1]; Ensure all refrigerated food is kept together in the same bag [1]; Do not buy frozen foods if you can't get them home quickly as they will defrost [1]; Use a collection service to get refrigerated food home as quickly as possible [1]; Use a home delivery service to get refrigerated food straight from refrigerated transport into your fridge [1]; Take the quickest route home so that refrigerated food is out of the fridge for as short a time as possible [1]; Store refrigerated food in a fridge, if available, at work [1]; Buy food with good packaging to keep it in shape, avoid squashing etc., e.g. eggs [1]; Park car in a shaded cool spot/not sunny area to keep the internal temperature of the car down so that temperature gain in refrigerated food is kept to a minimum [1].

2. **Any six from**: Avoid cross contamination/transfer from raw meat to cooked meat products by: foods touching/blood and juices dripping/transferring by hands, work surfaces/knives or equipment [1]; Good personal hygiene of workers – hand washing/clean protective overalls [1]; Good hygiene during cooking and serving – cover and cool all cooked meat as rapidly as possible/don't prepare too far in advance/no exposure to flies etc. [1]; Use red chopping boards [1]; Avoid incorrect storage, i.e. room temperature instead of below 8°C/not covering meat/store in bottom of refrigerator to avoid drip contamination [1]; Storage – use stock rotation/stick to use-by date [1]; Thaw meat thoroughly before cooking [1]; Do not undercook meat or bacteria will not be killed in centre/use a temperature probe to make sure that the correct temperature needed to kill bacteria has been reached [1]; Chilling – allow meat to cool before putting it into chill cabinets or the freezer/90 mins to chill below 8°C/use a blast chiller to cool quickly [1]; Reheat to the correct temperature for a long enough period of time (over 72°C) [1]; Hot holding – make sure hot meat products are kept at a hot enough holding temperature (63°C) [1]; Freezing – do not refreeze meat once it has been defrosted [1].

Page 24: Preparing and Cooking Food

1. **Any three from**: Store food in the correct place [1] because this reduces the chance of cross contamination/microorganism growth [1]; Store food at the correct temperature [1] because microorganisms require specific temperatures to grow, therefore, keeping them out of their temperature-growth zone slows bacteria growth [1]; Store food for the correct period of time [1] because storing food for longer than recommended increases the likelihood of microorganisms being present and growing in the food [1]; Defrost frozen products thoroughly [1] so that they can then be cooked to the correct temperature throughout – this ensures microorganisms in the middle of the food are killed [1]; Wear clean clothes when handling food [1] because this reduces the chances of contamination from clothing, e.g. dirt or pet hair [1]; Wash hands thoroughly and regularly, especially after using the toilet, handling rubbish or handling raw or different food products [1] because this reduces the chances of contamination from these sources [1]; Use clean equipment/clean the equipment thoroughly [1] because this reduces the chances of cross contamination

if the equipment was used for a different food item, e.g. raw and cooked meats [1]; Do not allow raw food to come into contact with cooked food [1] so that the chances of cross contamination are reduced [1]; Do not cough/sneeze over food or touch your nose/face when handling food [1] because this can spread bacteria/viruses present, leading to an increased risk of food poisoning [1]; Do not let animals or pests enter the food preparation area [1] because animals carry diseases and bacteria which can infect the food, and their hairs may also infect the food [1]; Cook food to the correct temperature [1] to ensure that microorganisms are killed to stop their growth [1]; Cook food for the correct amount of time [1] so that the food is cooked all the way through, with no cold spots – this ensures that all parts of the food have been heated to at least above the danger zone for microorganism growth [1]; Cool leftover food quickly [1] so that the time in which the food is in the danger zone is minimised, thereby reducing the chances of contamination and microorganism growth [1]; Reheat food only once [1] as food that has been cooked and cooled previously gives microorganisms more opportunity to grow [1]; Tie hair back/do not wear jewellery/false nails [1] to reduce the likelihood of these objects or bacteria from them falling into the food and contaminating it [1]. (**1 mark for each point made, with an additional 1 mark for explanation of each point – both must be given – up to a maximum of 6 marks.**)

2. **Any four from**: Avoid cross contamination [1]; Check use-by date [1]; Use appropriately colour-coded board/separate equipment [1]; Cook thoroughly/use a probe to check the temperature [1]; Once cooked serve immediately [1]; Use a clean knife/chopping board/work surface for preparation [1]; Wash hands before preparing/after handling [1]; Wear protective clothing/make sure hair is tied back [1].

3. **Any eight from**: Store foods according to their correct storage instructions [1]; Use correct cooking utensils for different foods [1]; Clean equipment and surfaces (with an antibacterial spray) [1]; Use within the best-before and use-by dates [1]; Clear up goods that have spilled [1]; Cook foods according to their cooking instructions [1]; Wash your hands [1]; Tie hair back [1]; Take off jewellery [1]; Remove nail varnish [1]; Wear a clean apron [1]; Take extra care with food preparation when ill [1]; Cover food [1]; Avoid coughing/sneezing over food [1]; Handle food as little as possible [1]; Cover cuts with waterproof dressing [1]; Avoid cross-contamination [1].

Page 25: Food Choices

1. Vegetarians eat fish. False [1]; Buddhists eat pork. False [1]; Sikhs don't eat beef. True [1]
2. c) [1]
3. c) [1]
4. **Any three from**: For health reasons [1]; For religious reasons [1]; Ethics – against cruelty to animals [1]; Ethics – against over-using the Earth's resources [1]; Don't like meat [1]; Born into a vegetarian family [1].
5. a) Lacto-vegetarians do not eat: meat/fish/eggs/non-vegetarian cheese/gelatine (from bones) [1]; which involves killing the animal [1]; but do eat animal products such as milk/cream/yogurt, etc. [1]
    b) Vegans do not eat anything sourced from animals [1]; such as: meat/fish/honey/gelatine/milk/milk products (cheese, butter, yogurt, cream) [1]; but do eat plant-based foods [1]

Page 26: British and International Cuisine

1. b) [1]
2. Wensleydale [1]
3. a) Cornish pasty [1]; hotpot [1]
    b) bouillabaisse [1]; Quiche Lorraine [1]
    c) tortilla [1]; paella [1]
    d) Peking duck [1]; chow mein [1]
    e) pakora [1]; dhal [1]
    f) minestrone [1]; focaccia [1]
4. **Answers depend on student's choice of country**

Page 27: Sensory Evaluation

1. smell [1]
2. a) [1]
3. a) Quiet area [1]; Invite people to taste [1]; Provide: water to cleanse palate [1]; Coded sample of food [1]; Clean eating implements, if needed [1]; Use a recording sheet [1].
    b) Testing two similar food products [1]; Three samples used but two the same [1]; All samples coded differently [1]; Aim is to try to identify the 'odd one out' [1].
    c) Name of product: any suitable name [1]
       Samples to trial: any suitable answer, e.g. 15% fat minced beef [1]; 5% fat minced beef [1].

Page 28: Food Labelling

1. c) [1]
2. b) [1]
3. a) Guideline Daily Amount [1]
    b) As a percentage [1]; Per portion [1]; Per 100 g of food [1]
    c) **Any six from**: Weight or volume ('e'approximate weight) [1]; Ingredients list (from largest to smallest) [1]; Allergen information [1]; GM (Genetically Modified) ingredients [1]; Date mark and storage [1]; Cooking instructions – to ensure food is safe to eat [1]; Place of origin [1]; Name and address of manufacturer (in case of complaint) [1]; Lot or batch mark (for traceability) [1]; Nutritional information on pre-packaged foods [1].
4. b) [1]

Page 29: Factors Affecting Food Choice

1. b) [1]
2. c) [1]
3. a) Exercise improves cardiovascular and bone health [1]; Exercise helps to maintain a healthy weight [1]; Exercise improves self-confidence [1]; Exercise develops new social skills if taken with other people, e.g. team sports, aerobics classes [1].
    b) The Eatwell Guide [1]
    c) Variety of flavours [1]; Variety of textures [1]; Variety of colours [1].
    d) **Any four from**: The type of work done by people in the household will affect their appetites [1]; The number of hours worked by people in the household will affect their appetites [1]; The travelling (commuting) time of members of the household will affect the amount of time available for the preparation and consumption of food [1]; The pastimes of individuals will affect their appetite and the amount of time available for shopping, preparing and cooking food [1]; Whoever is in charge of the planning and cooking of food will influence the types of food bought and consumed [1]; The available income for buying food will affect the types of foods eaten [1]; If someone is vegetarian/vegan [1]; If someone has a food allergy/intolerance [1]

Page 30: Food and the Environment

1. At each stage of a product's lifecycle energy [1] is needed to process [1], transport [1] and dispose [1] of the product; carbon dioxide [1] is produced as a byproduct of energy use. The carbon footprint [1] is the calculation of the carbon dioxide produced throughout a product's life.
2. Deforestation [1] occurs when trees are cut down. Cleared land is used as pasture [1] for livestock [1] and plantations [1] of commodities and settlements. Deforested regions typically suffer soil erosion [1] and frequently degrade into wasteland [1].
3. Wise shopping and planning ahead reduces the amount of food bought in the first place [1]; FIFO (first-in first-out storage) reduces food wasted [1]; Only prepare the food you actually need, so nothing is needlessly thrown away [1]; Use food before it goes out of date, so that food does not have to be thrown away for safety reasons [1]; Use leftover food to make other dishes, thereby avoiding having to throw leftover food out [1]; Do home composting so that any food you have to throw out does not have to be transported to a landfill site [1].
4. **Any two suitable answers**, e.g.: Bubble and squeak [1]; Rissoles [1]; Soup [1]; Corned beef hash [1].

Page 31: Food Provenance and Production Methods

1. When traceability is fully available, trust is built between the retailer and the consumer [1]; Other criteria in which the consumer has an interest, such as ensuring the food is organic, vegetarian, specific allergen free, Kosher or Halal can be guaranteed via traceability [1]; This ensures that consumers can have confidence in the food they purchase [1]; Where there is a risk to public health, manufacturers may need to isolate sources, so traceability is practical [1].
2. Battery, **any two from**: Large numbers of hens kept in massive buildings designed to maximise growth [1]; Fed on high nutrient feeds over a short period of time [1]; Antibiotics and growth enhancers widely used [1].
    Free range: These hens have access to outdoor areas for part of their lives [1]; They do not live in cages [1].
    Barn, **any two from**: These hens live in an environment similar to intensively-reared animals but have access to natural light from windows [1]; They live in a lower density of animals per square metre [1]; They have access to environment enrichment such as fresh straw [1].
    Organic: hens are fed on products free from chemical or synthetic treatments that have relied on natural compost and manure for fertilisers [1]; Often kept out of doors with complete freedom [1].
3. b); c) [1]

Page 32: Sustainability of Food

1. CO_2/carbon dioxide [1]
2. **Any three from**: Increase crop diversity [1]; Improve soil organics by using animal waste [1]; Change the dependence on fossil fuels to transport foods [1]; Tackle deforestation issues [1]; Put in irrigation systems in drier areas [1]; Look at crop rotation to reduce soil erosion and the general health of crops [1]; Prevent soil erosion from winds, high rainfall and flooding [1].
3. a) **Any two from**: The Fairtrade logo means that the farmer in a developing country who produced

the goods gets a realistic income [1]; Investment in the local community takes place [1]; There are better working conditions for the producing farmer [1]; A fair price is paid for the goods [1]; Sustainable production methods are used [1].

   b) Possible answers, **any two from**: Chocolate; Tea; Coffee; Bananas **(two answers needed for 1 mark)**.

4. The Red Tractor logo tells us that the food has been produced, processed and packed to the Red Tractor standards [1]; The flag on the Red Tractor logo shows the country of origin [1]; Red Tractor labelling assures good standards of food hygiene and safety [1]; Red Tractor labelling assures high standards of equipment used in production [1]; Red Tractor standards assure good standards of animal health and welfare [1]; Environmental issues are respected by Red Tractor suppliers [1]; Red Tractor standards ensure responsible use of pesticides [1]. Any product with the Red Tractor logo can be traced from farm to fork [1].

5. Livestock, especially cows, produce methane gas [1]; Methane gas is 20 times more harmful than CO_2 [1], with cows producing more Green House Gases (GHG) than the entire world's transport.

Page 33: Food Production

1. In homogenised milk, the milk is forced through tiny holes in a machine [1]; This breaks up the fat and disperses it, and it doesn't reform as a layer [1]

2. The cream may separate   [1]

3. a) **Any three suitable answers, e.g. three from**: Red Leicester [1]; Cheddar [1]; Cheshire [1]; Lancashire [1]; Wensleydale [1]; Stilton [1]; Caerphilly [1].

   b) **Any three suitable answers, e.g. three from**: Brie [1]; Camembert [1]; Fromage frais [1]; Roquefort [1]; Saint Agur [1].

4. Possible answers, **any six from**: White [1]; Granary [1]; Wheatmeal [1]; Wholemeal [1]; Brown [1]; Spelt [1]; Self-raising [1]; Plain [1]; Strong [1]; 00 pasta flour [1].

5. Bread is made by mixing strong flour (which is high in gluten [1]) with liquid [1] and a raising agent such as yeast [1]. The yeast ferments with sugar [1] and warm water, and then when added to the flour and salt it makes a dough [1]. The dough is then worked by a process called kneading [1]. The dough is then allowed to rise further by standing covered in a warm environment. This is known as proving [1]. The bread dough is then shaped and finished with a glaze [1] before baking.

6. 00 flour [1]; Made from durum wheat [1]

Page 34: Food Processing

1. High temperature [1]; Low temperature [1]; Drying [1]; Chemical [1].

2. Method, **any one of**: Freezing [1]; Sugar [1]; Vinegar [1]; Oven-drying [1]. Shelf life, **corresponding one of**: Freezing – food is preserved for up to one year in temperatures between –18°C and –29°C [1]; Sugar – fruit is preserved with sugar, e.g. jam, for a couple of years [1]; Vinegar – vegetables can be preserved for up to two years by immersion in vinegar [1]; Oven drying – a warm oven can be used to dry foods slowly and they can then be stored in an airtight container for several months [1].

3. Low temperature does not affect nutritional value [1]

4. Meat/fish is 'cooked' by exposing it to heat from wood fires [1]; This gives it a distinctive smoky taste [1].

5. Fruit could be preserved in jars of alcohol – usually brandy [1]; Fruit could be added to sugar to make jams [1]; Vegetables could be pickled in vinegar to make pickles or chutneys and stored in jars [1]; Vegetables could be stored in jars in a brine(salt) solution [1].

6. They are pickled in vinegar with spices [1]

7. It is salted [1]; It can also be smoked [1]

Page 35-51 Practice Exam Paper 1

Section A

1.1	B	[1]
1.2	D	[1]
1.3	C	[1]
1.4	A	[1]
2.1	D	[1]
2.2	C	[1]
2.3	C	[1]
2.4	A	[1]
3.1	B	[1]
3.2	A	[1]
3.3	C	[1]
3.4	C	[1]
4.1	C	[1]
4.2	A	[1]
4.3	B	[1]
4.4	C	[1]
5.1	C	[1]
5.2	A	[1]
5.3	B	[1]
5.4	C	[1]

Section B

6.1 **Any four from**: When sugar is consumed it is broken down by the bacteria on the plaque found on teeth [1]; By this process, the sugar turns into acid [1]; This acid causes the tooth enamel to dissolve [1]; With damaged or non-existent enamel, the tooth is weakened [1]; As a result of weakened enamel, a cavity (hole) develops in

the tooth [1]; The whole tooth can become damaged as a result of the cavity [1]; Pain may result because of the damaged tooth [1]; Fillings will have to be applied to the damaged tooth or a complete extraction will be necessary [1].

6.2 **Any four from**: Avoid sugary drinks – always check labels or use sugar apps to find out information about sugar content [1]; Choose water instead of a sugary drink [1]; Reduce consumption of high sugar foods, cakes, biscuits, chocolate and sweets [1]: Do not give sweets as a reward to children [1]; Avoid breakfast cereals coated with sugar, which are typically marketed to children [1]; Reduce the sugar content of foods when doing home baking – use natural fruits or dried fruits as an alternative to sugar [1]; Teach children about the dangers of overconsumption of sugar – help them to make the right decisions [1]; Parents should teach children by example – by not eating too much sugar themselves [1]; Check school food policy on sugar and on sugar in school dinners [1].

6.3 Named disease, **any two from**: Diabetes (Type 2) [1]; Obesity [1]; Coronary heart disease [1].
Causes – diabetes type 2: High blood sugar [1]; Lack of insulin/no insulin to regulate sugar levels [1].
Causes – obesity, **any two from**: Sugar is high in calories [1]; Over-consumption leads to excess fat forming [1]; Under skin and around internal organs [1].
Causes – coronary heart disease, **any two from**: High blood sugar level leads to diabetes type 2, which more than doubles the risk of developing coronary heart disease [1]; Lining of blood vessels become thick, which restricts blood flow [1]; Heart has to work harder to get oxygen around the body [1].

6.4 Two other carbohydrate groups: Starch [1]; Non-Starch Polysaccharide [1].
Examples – starch, **any two from**: Bread [1]; Pasta [1]; Potatoes [1]; Rice [1]; Breakfast cereals [1].
Examples – Non-Starch Polysaccharide, **any two from**: Wholegrain cereals [1]; Wholemeal bread [1]; Wholegrain breakfast cereals, e.g. bran flakes, Weetabix, shredded wheat, porridge oats [1]; Wholemeal pasta [1]; Wholemeal flour [1]; Any named fruit [1]; Any named vegetable [1]; Dried fruit [1]; Nuts [1]; Seeds [1]; Beans/peas/lentils [1].
(2 marks for naming each type of carbohydrate group, 2 marks for two examples of each carbohydrate group, up to a maximum of 4 marks, 6 marks in total for the question)

6.5 **Any six from**: Protein [1] – for growth, maintenance and repair of the body [1]; Some fat [1] – to provide concentrated sources of energy, and to aid brain function [1]; Carbohydrate (starch) [1] – for slow release energy [1]; Calcium [1] – for strong bones and teeth [1]; Iron [1] – for the formation of haemoglobin in red blood cells [1]. Fluoride [1] – to strengthen teeth [1]; Vitamin C [1] – to aid the absorption of iron and to build connective tissues [1]; Vitamin D [1] – to aid the absorption of calcium [1]; Reference to current nutritional guidelines [1] and the Eatwell Guide [1].

7.1 Herb – bay leaf [1]; Spice – peppercorns [1]

7.2 Milk contains lactose [1]; Lactose intolerance means that an individual is allergic to/cannot tolerate lactose in their diet [1]

7.3 Step 1: **Any three from:** hob heat [1]; Conduction though pan [1]; Pan base heat [1]; Liquid heat by convection [1].

7.4 **Any three from:** Starch in flour [1]; Swells [1]; Agitated beaten [1]; Smooth gelatinisation [1].

7.5 Choux pastry: Function – to give structure to the pastry [1]. Description – flour is used to thicken the pastry dough [1], the flour forms structure [1]
Bread: Function – to provide gluten [1]. Description – **Any two from:** makes the dough [1], stretchy dough lets yeast work [1], sets on cooking [1]

8.1 **Any four from:** Pasteurised milk [1] – this extends shelf life [1]; Skimmed, pasteurised [1] – all or most of the cream is removed [1]; Semi-skimmed, pasteurised [1]; some of the cream is removed [1]; Ultra-Heat Treated (UHT), also known as long life milk [1] – has a shelf life of up to six months [1]; Sterilised, homogenised [1] – has a longer shelf life/has a slightly caramel flavour [1];
Dried [1]; Evaporating the water, leaving a fine powder [1].
Canned; evaporated [1] – Water evaporated off. Sweet and concentrated. Homogenised. Sealed in cans and sterilised [1].
Condensed [1] is evaporated milk that hasn't been sterilised; added sugar; very thick [1].
(1 mark for the name of each type of milk and 1 mark for each reason.)

8.2 **Any two from:** Butter [1] – cream is churned to make butter [2]; Cream [1] – the fat removed from milk is used [2]; Cheese [1] – this is milk in its solid form [2]; Yoghurt [1] – milk has a bacteria culture added to it [2].

9.1 **Any eight from:** Energy kcals comparison using data [1] better choice is sauce B [1]; Unsaturated fat comparison using data [1] better choice is B [1]; Saturated fat comparison using data [1] better choice is B [1]; Sugar comparison using data [1] better choice is B [1]; Comments about ingredients relating to healthy choices: Vegetables low in fat [1]; Vegetables low in kcals [1];

Vegetables should be included in a healthy diet [1]; Obese person should choose foods that are: Low in kcal [1]; Low in fat [1]; Include vegetables [1]. **(The eight relevant points chosen must avoid repetition.)**

10.1 Victoria sandwich not rising, **any two from:** Too much sugar, causing the gluten to be over-softened so that it collapses [1]; Too much raising agent, causing the gluten to overstretch and collapse [1]; Undercooking, caused by the wrong temperature or cooking time [1]; Opening the oven door before the gluten has set, so the heavy cold air makes it sink [1]. Lumpy cheese sauce, **any two from:** Liquid and starch not blended before cooking [1]; Insufficient stirring during the cooking [1]; Cheese added when sauce is cooled so does not melt [1]; Roux not cooked sufficiently [1]; Incorrect proportion of ingredients [1].

10.2 High risk foods are easily contaminated by bacteria [1] and so can cause food poisoning if not correctly stored at a temperature of 0°C-5°C and cooked thoroughly [1]. They have a short shelf life [1]. High risk foods include foods which aren't cooked before being eaten so, if contaminated, bacteria will not be destroyed e.g. cream, cooked meats, raw fish (sushi) [1]. Protein foods such as meat, milk, fish and eggs are high risk, as are cooked rice and lentils [1]. Other high risk foods are moist foods like gravy and soup and unpasteurised foods e.g. soft cheese made from unpasteurised milk [1].

Pages 52-68 Practice Exam Paper 2

Section A

1.1 B		[1]
1.2 D		[1]
1.3 B		[1]
1.4 A		[1]
2.1 C		[1]
2.2 B		[1]
2.3 A		[1]
2.4 B		[1]
3.1 A		[1]
3.2 D		[1]
3.3 B		[1]
3.4 D		[1]
4.1 B		[1]
4.2 C		[1]
4.3 D		[1]
4.4 C		[1]
5.1 C		[1]
5.2 A		[1]
5.3 C		[1]
5.4 D		[1]

Section B

6.1 **Any six from:** Three energy-giving macronutrients are identified: Carbohydrates are present within

breakfast in the form of starch and sugars [1]. Specifically, they will be provided from the bread and the hot chocolate drink [1]. Energy may be released in different ways depending upon the type of food. In this particular instance there will be a slow release of energy from the wholemeal bread [1].
Fat: Present within the breakfast in the form of saturated and unsaturated fats [1]. Specifically provided from the sausages, streaky bacon, whole milk and cooking fats [1]. There is a lot of fat in this breakfast that will deliver high energy content [1].
Protein: Protein is a secondary source of energy and is available in the egg, sausage and milk [1].
Any other relevant and correct response can be credited.

6.2 **Any 12 from:** High fat diets linked to high cholesterol [1], which attaches to sides of arteries, narrows them, restricts blood flow, blocks arteries [1], can lead to Coronary Heart Disease (CHD) [1]. Linked to High Blood Pressure, angina and stroke [1]. High fat diets are high energy possibly leading to obesity [1], which causes both physical and psychological problems [1]. In addition to a high fat diet, there are several factors that often work together to contribute to ill health and increased future health risks, these are some possible responses, but other relevant factors should be rewarded as appropriate: Lack of physical activity [1]; Psychological influences – for example, may use eating as a coping mechanism for dealing with emotional problems, such as family break-up, etc. [1]; Genetics – for example, family history of overweight people due to genetic reasons [1], family history of medical conditions [1]; Socio-economic issues – for example, low income backgrounds [1], lack of time, resources, knowledge, skills [1], reliance on fast foods [1], parents working and effect of each of these on food choices [1]. Also note that there are unhealthy dietary options which do not reflect current government dietary guidelines, such as the Eatwell Guide [1].

6.3 **Any three from:** Energy linked to Kcal [2]; Warmth/insulation linked to body fat [2]; Protection of internal organs – kidneys [2]; Source of fat-soluble vitamins A, D, E and K linked to relevant food sources [2]; Formation of cell membranes – maintenance and good health [2].

6.4 Saturated fat, description of make-up, **any two from:** Contains the maximum amounts of hydrogen [1]; Molecule made up of single bonds (diagram could be drawn) [1]; Solid fat [1]; Solid animal fat [1].

Examples, **any two from**: Butter [1]; Lard [1]; Ghee [1]; Dripping [1]; Suet [1]; Cream [1]; Coconut oil [1]. Unsaturated fat, description of make-up, **any two from**: Able to accept more hydrogen [1]; More than one double bond in the molecule (diagram could be drawn) [1]; Vegetable source – oils [1].

Examples, **any two from**: Vegetable oil [1]; Corn oil [1]; Olive oil [1]; Rape seed oil [1]; Sunflower oil [1]; Groundnut oil [1]; Sesame oil [1]; Some fish oils [1]; Commercial fats, e.g. Flora products [1].

7.1 Flavouring – lemon zest [1]; Spice – cinnamon [1]

7.2 Butter is a saturated fat and not a healthy choice [2]

7.3 Oven is pre-heated [1] convection currents [1] baking tray heats shortbread by conduction [1].

7.4 **Any three from**: Fat melts [1]; Fat is then absorbed by flour [1]; Surface sugars caramelise [1]; Shortbread crisps [1].

7.5 Pastry tarts: Function – Shortening [1] Description – Fat coats the flour grains, preventing gluten development [1] so the cooked texture is short and crumbly [1]. Sponge cake: Function – Aeration [1] Description – When fat and sugar are creamed air is trapped [1] so the cooked texture is light and fluffy [1].

8.1 **Any six from**: Farmers' markets contribute to thriving local economies [1]; Sustainable livelihoods [1]; Protects the diversity of both plants and animals [1]; Welfare of farmed and wild species [1]; Farmers' markets avoid dependence on fossil fuels to transport foods around the world [1]; Farmers' markets sell quality locally grown products that support local businesses and farmers [1]; Farmers' markets provide fresh produce [1]; Farmers' markets avoid the need for extra packaging or the use of preservation techniques [1].

8.2 **Any three from**: Battery (intensive farmed) [1]; large numbers of hens kept in massive buildings/designed to maximise egg production/on high nutrient feeds/short period of growth time/antibiotics/growth enhancers/fertilisers and pesticides being widely used/poor quality eggs [1]. Barn [1]; environment similar to intensively-reared animals/have access to natural light from windows/live in a lower density of animals per square metre/better quality eggs than intensive farmed [1]. Free range [1]; allows animals or poultry access to outdoor areas for part of lives/behave as they would in nature, digging and foraging/hens that are free-range produce eggs that are more nutritious and tasty [1]. Organic [1]; hens reared naturally without help from any chemical or synthetic treatments/rely on natural composts and manure for fertilisers for growing their feed/are GM free/no proof that organic food is more nutritious/buying organic food is a lifestyle choice/organic and free-range farming more ethical/lower negative environmental impact [1].

8.3 **Any two from**: Hens' eggs must carry a stamp with a number indicating whether they have been produced in an organic, free-range, barn or cage system [1]; Egg boxes must clearly state: 'eggs from caged hens', 'barn eggs' or 'free range' [1]; Eggs must carry the lion mark [1]

9.1 **Any eight from**: Both [1] of these sausages are gluten- free [1] so can be eaten by a coeliac because they will not contain gluten [1]; Saturated fat comparison using data [1], better choice is sausage A [1]; Energy kcals comparison using data [1], better choice is sausage A [1]; Dietary fibre comparison using data [1], better choice is sausage A [1]; Coeliacs would look for the gluten-free label or symbol [1]; Comments should be included about ingredients relating to healthy choices: Vegetables are low in kcals/vegetables should be included in a healthy diet [1]; People should choose foods that are: Low in kcal [1], Low in fat [1]; Contain protein [1]; Contain dietary fibre [1]; Are low in salt [1]; Are low in total fat [1]. **(The eight relevant points chosen must avoid repetition.)**

10.1 Bread not rising, **any two from**: Liquid too warm it kills the yeast [1]; Room is too cold during proving [1]; Insufficient proving time [1]; Too much salt added, which kills the yeast [1]; Insufficient liquid used [1]. Quiche not setting, **any two from**: Not enough egg mixture to set the quiche [1]; Too much liquid (milk) [1]; Oven temperature too low [1]; Insufficient cooking time [1].

10.2 **Any six from**: Follow storage instructions on label to prevent food spoilage [1]; Chilled foods should be stored in a refrigerator between 0°–5 °C as this slows down bacterial growth [1]; Use a fridge thermometer to ensure the fridge is kept at a safe temperature, which should be between 0° and 5 °C [1]; Cooked foods should be stored above raw foods to prevent cross contamination [1]; Cover foods in the refrigerator to prevent cross contamination [1]; Check foods frequently for signs of decay and that they are within their use-by dates, as bacterial growth can lead to food poisoning [1]; Keep refrigerators clean to prevent microbial growth [1]; Do not overload the fridge as air needs to circulate to keep the food cool [1]; Do not put warm foods in a fridge as this will raise its temperature [1]; Store frozen foods in the freezer below −18°C as this prevents food thawing out and bacteria becoming active [1]; Do not re-freeze food once it has defrosted as bacterial multiplication may have taken place as the food warmed up [1]; Rotate stock/check use-by dates to ensure the oldest food is used first – this prevents dry foods becoming rancid or infested by pests [1]; Store non-perishable foods in cool dry conditions, to keep them fresh [1].

Notes